HORSE FARMING THROUGH THE SEASONS

by

Herbert L. Day

HUTTON PRESS
1991

Published by the Hutton Press Ltd.,
130 Canada Drive, Cherry Burton,
Beverley, East Yorkshire, HU17 7SB

Printed and bound by
Clifford Ward & Co. (Bridlington) Ltd.
55 West Street, Bridlington, East Yorkshire
YO15 3DZ

ISBN 1 872167 28 4

CONTENTS

Chapter 1

Martinmas was a day to remember

The method of hiring single farm workers for a year as practiced by farmers in the past may be considered today as degrading. Yet in the hungry 1920s there were unemployed industrial workers who would have accepted a guaranteed year's work and their board regardless. They had no choice — there were too many countrymen out of work. Martinmas Day, 23 November, was a red letter day in the lives of the hired workers. It was their pay day of the year and they could leave the farm, their place of employment, for good. On the other hand they could also be given the opportunity to re-engage for another year.

November was a relaxed period — harvest and wheat sowing had been completed and roots lifted. Ploughing was the order of the day and this caused little anxiety. Hired lads began to count the days to Martinmas. When the great day arrived, instead of ploughing, they were ordered to fill every available space in the buildings with straw and fill the turnip house. This was for the benefit of the skeletal staff at work during Martinmas week. When this work was completed, the horses were fed, groomed and bedded with straw. This was to be the last time for the men who did not intend to return and there was regret at leaving horses they had worked and cared for. During Martinmas week in every country town a day was arranged for hirings to take place, usually on the recognised market day. On such an occasion the town was full of country folk — farmers, foremen and their wives, single workers and also tradesmen from the surrounding villages.

Previous to 1920 there were no bus services in operation and in most areas no convenient railway. A long walk was involved for many of the villagers attending the hirings and it was one of the rare occasions they visited their local town. Relatives and friends met who had not seen each other since the previous Martinmas. They congregated in the market place to exchange news and this was one of the most pleasant aspects experienced on a hirings day. It was one of the busiest days of the year for the shopkeepers. Clothes and boots were bought for the year ahead. Also watches and pocket knives. Hired horsemen were always interested in the brasses on display in a saddler's shop window.

Bargaining took place between master and man regarding a year's wage. When agreement was reached, the worker received a 'fist', a small sum of money to seal the bargain. When a lad had completed his first year and received his wage he became independent of his family. After he had paid for his new rig-out he had little left for pocket money, yet he contrived to make this last until Martinmas came round again. In those days independence was a noticeable characteristic of country folk, who considered accepting charity as being degrading.

After the business of hiring and shopping, all the fun of the fair could be enjoyed. Sites had been found in the town to erect stalls, swings and a steam roundabout. In an era when farm men worked long hours and pleasures were few, it was a day to remember and discuss during the dark winter months ahead.

Pickering, Rise Carr Farm, 1920. Pickering situated on the fringe of the North Yorkshire Moors, has become commercial to such an extent it has lost its old-world charm. Today situated in the town centre is a large car park, a place for vehicles mainly concerned with pleasure. Yet in the past on this site there was a busy goods yard. The only indication left of this by-gone industry is the shell of a building which is now the Old Granary Café. In those days it was a warehouse owned by Sammy Baker, the local agricultural merchant. I can recall visiting this place with a horse and cart to collect a load of cattle cakes. The year was 1916, and I was fourteen. The turnout was the property of my Uncle Bill Goforth who owned Rise Carr Farm where I lived from the age of 10. It was the first time I had been trusted with such an errand and I was as proud as 'Punch' when driving *Daisy* along Hungate. On arrival at Toon End I turned right onto the Malton road and continued my journey until I came to the crossroads known as Bean Sheaf Corner. I then turned left down Bean Sheaf Lane and at the end of this was a gate entry to our farm. I made my way to the barn where the cattle cakes were stored and as I expected, my grandad was waiting to help me unload. Shortly after I had left Kirby Misperton school the previous year 1915, he had taken me in hand and taught me to plough, handle a pair of horses and also load hay or corn sheaves on a wagon. At the hirings fair held at Pickering in 1916 a farmer engaged me to be one of his horse lads.

Daisy **Shire mare with foal at foot.** Uncle Bill emigrated to Australia in 1873 and 17 years later he returned and bought Rise Carr Farm. This enabled him to provide a home for his sister Ella, his father Jonathan in retirement, and employment for his brother Bob. I arrived at the farm after the death of my mother and it became my home. In later years I always returned to spend my Martinmas weeks. On each Sunday we had roast duck for dinner. Her mother had provided a similar meal for her four sons when they had returned to their place, and she had continued the tradition. Bill kept 4 working mares *Bonnie*, *Darling*, *Blossom* and *Daisy* and the last two each bred a foal for several years, but we lost *Blossom* in 1914. This particular night she was due to foal and Bill was "cat napping" on a chair in the kitchen. He visited the mare in the loose box every hour and at 2.0 a.m. he found her lying quiet and serene, her new born foal standing near. Before Bill visited the mare again she suffered an attack of colic and her contortions proved fatal. After I returned from school I prepared the loose box with a bed of clean dry straw. This particular evening *Blossom* had walked as regal as a queen from the stable to the loose box. After I had closed the door I little dreamed she would never walk through it again.

Ready for departure to the corn market. Jonathan never lost his nerve when concerned with horses. He drove *Jess* yoked to the trap until he was 80. Bill bought the mare at a sale and she turned out to be a jibber. One market day at Pickering when Jonathan was collecting a bag of flour from Strickland the grocer, only kerb stones prevented *Jess* from backing the trap through the shop window. The following happened one sunny day in June 1915. Jonathan had invited me to accompany him on one of his trips round the countryside. We had 'yoked up' and were seated side by side ready to move off. Instead *Jess* backed the trap until it came into contact with the garden hedge. The whip appeared in Jonathan's hand and he galloped the mare several times round the paddock. Bill who saw this performance said later the trap was turning on one wheel. I clung to the trap with my eyes closed and when I opened them *Jess* was travelling down Bean Sheaf Lane at a speed she had never reached before. We were fortunate because on our return we found one of the shafts had splintered. Jonathan called it a day and the trap became obsolete. Bill sold *Jess* and in July I left school.

Village pump, Kirby Misperton, 1900. In my boyhood days farmers and cottages obtained water for household purposes free, except for the cost of a pump but conditions in their homes were primitive. No piped water was available, therefore it was impossible to install a hot water system —a bathroom with modern conveniences or a flushed toilet. Water was carried from a well into the home and waste water carried out. Outside out kitchen door there was a shallow depression, surfaced with cement and in the centre was a sink. Waste water poured into it, drained into a ditch at the opposite side of the stackyard. It was worthwhile to collect in a butt the water which ran off the roof. As soft water it was ideal for personal hygiene or for washing clothes. No doubt before a farmstead was built a water diviner was engaged. He carried a forked hazel twig which turned in his hand when a source of water was found. On every farm there was at least one well, but village homes were not so fortunate for those with a well were in the minority. In every village there was a pump sited about half way along the street and for some it was a long walk. This meant using a yoke; a piece of wood shaped to fit a carrier's neck and shoulders, with a bucket suspended from each end of a chain.

Bullocks feeding from a tumbler, Rise Carr Farm, 1914. The water we required for household purposes and to satisfy stock, was pumped out of a well situated in the garden. It was so deep that even during a hot summer the water remained cool and the well was never dry. It was sited near an entry to the stackyard where a large tank had been placed. Wooden roof spouting was fixed to a wall, which could be connected to the spout of the pump. When this was being operated, water flowed along the spouting into the tank. It had to be refilled several times each day in the winter when stock was kept in the buildings. During school holidays I operated the pump, and to do so, I had to stand on a box to lift the heavy handle and use my full weight to press it down. Many times when I expected the tank to be full I found bullocks drinking the water at the same rate as I pumped it. A second well had been sunk in the paddock next to the stackyard, but the water was unfit for human consumption. Ironically, this pump could be operated with ease, but it had to be primed first. A bucket of water was poured into the top of the pump and the handle was then worked up and down furiously until the water flowed. On a threshing day it was my job to ensure there was a sufficient supply of water in the barrel near the engine and I obtained it from the well in the paddock.

A carrier's cart. A countryman getting on in years may look back to his early years through rose-tinted glasses. This is understandable because those days had a lot to commend them. Pilfering and stealing in a village was almost unknown. Farm granaries and other buildings were never locked. There was little concern if through forgetfulness a farm house or cottage door remained unlocked throughout the night. When darkness enveloped the countryside, females of all ages walked the bylanes without fear. A tailor made to measure the clothes requested by the farming community and villagers. Practically every commodity they required was stocked by the village store. The village carrier, his horse-drawn cart especially designed for the purpose, visited the local market town several days each week. He provided a service for the villagers and collected their requirements not on sale in the stores. A road-man who lived in the village ensured its cleanliness and he maintained the by-roads. An ex-wagoner, he used a scythe to cut the long grass and he kept the grips open which drained the water off the roads. He also edged the grass verges as straight as the furrows he had ploughed in days gone by. A pleasant scene to the eye missing from many roads today.

Smiddy Hill, Pickering, from "Toon End". The business conducted on a Monday Market day at Pickering, bears little resemblance to that which was transacted when I was a lad. Farmers no longer submit samples of their grain for sale to corn factors. Horses and traps, farmers conveyances, entering or leaving the town, will never be witnessed again. When the cattle market was demolished the buying and selling of farm stock came to an end. Changes have take place at 'Toon End', a roundabout has been built and the road made wider. The house where Jack and Dick Bouldry 'shoemakers' lived and their workshop were demolished in the process. Their trade name was false, for in their day no shoes were made. The brothers specialised in making boots for farm workers and they guaranteed them 'water tight'. A customer's feet were measured and allowances made for bunions. The first pair they made cost 15 shillings — men's size £1 a pair. I followed the advice given to me by my grandfather and ensured they were made to a size which enabled me to wear two pairs of hand-knitted socks, increased protection for my feet against frosts and should they sweat in the summer, there were two layers of wool to absorb the moisture.

Surplus branches for kindling. Hedges were essential on a mixed farm to prevent stock from straying into fields under crops. When gaps appeared these were plugged with stakes and then the hedge was allowed to grow freely for several years. When the branches reached a certain height, the oldest were removed and the rest were 'cut and laid'. Each one was trimmed and then cut to the required length. A sliced cut was made near the bottom of each branch and this enabled the hedger to lay each one at a slight upward angle. It was important to make this cut as shallow as possible, to ensure each branch maintained a good connection with its roots. Each branch, as it was laid, overlapped the previous one laid and small stakes were used to hold them in position. This work was done in the winter when the sap was at its lowest ebb. In the spring, shoots appeared on the laid branches which became the foundation for a good young hedge. The only heat available in a cottage or farmhouse was that created by a coal fire. Bob cut and laid at least one hedge every winter, and the surplus branches were carted home to be cut into kindling to light fires.

Load of sheaves. The Malton/Pickering railway crossed our yard and separated 2 tillage fields from the rest. Entry to each one was over a crossing surfaced with sleepers and enclosed by 2 gates. These were often in use when a field was under cultivation and at harvest when empty and loaded waggons were constantly crossing the line. Bill laid down this procedure which we all practiced. If there wasn't a train in sight the gate at the opposite side was opened first to small traffic to cross without stopping; only then were the two gates shut. We never had an accident in this respect but we lost two dogs. Bob was ploughing an adjacent field when one went to sleep on the railway and was killed by a passing train. Four years later, the second dog *Punch* suffered a similar fate, but I was the ploughman. In 1920 I was third-lad at Grange Farm. Martinmas Day was drawing near and I had agreed to return for another year when I received a letter from Bill stating that Bob had suffered a leg injury and would I return and take his place. I had no option but to oblige him and I was surprised when I saw *Punch* in such a pitiful state, crippled with rheumatism, deaf and nearly blind. He rarely left his bed of straw in the barn. Yet one day he limped to the field where I was ploughing, and history was repeated. I carried his remains in a sack to the orchard where I buried them.

(From right to left) Third lad, wagoner's lad, wagoner, foreman. Last man in line was a labourer, and the horse an unbroken two-year old. Manor Farm was a typical Wold farm. The main revenue was obtained from the production of barley and breeding sheep for the fat stock market. The farm comprised 300 acres and the work force consisted of a foreman, 2 horsemen and 2 teenagers, who tilled the land and cared for the horses. A shepherd, a bullocky, and two labourers completed the force. The foreman was recognised as the "boss" and addressed as such. His main responsibilities were the organising of the labour force —cultivation, sowing the seed, and harvesting the crops. If the work was well in hand, the master never interfered with his arrangements. 12 horses were required, 6 stallions in each of the 2 stables. It was a recognised condition of employment that 6 horses should be the restricted number a man and a lad should care for. The wagoner was in charge of one stable, and third lad the other. He was so named because he was the third in seniority, the foreman being first, and the wagoner second. When ploughing was in progress the wagoner was in the lead, followed by the third lad and their respective lads. I was the youngest, referred to as "least lad". My pair of horses were the last in the procession to the field. I was the last to wash before a meal, which meant making up for lost time at the table.

A group of hired horsemen at the turn of the century. The Wagoner and "Thoddy" — the dialect word — were each responsible for the condition of the horses in their stable and the routine practiced was universal on all the Wold farms. Soon after 5.0 a.m. we were out of bed and on our way to the stable. When we opened the door there was bedlam. The horses whinnied, kicked the wooden partitions and stamped on the cobbled floor. These sounds were music to our ears — hungry horses were in good fettle. The noises subsided after thoddy had given each horse a feed of oats, and chaff. I had made a start to muck-out and when thoddy joined in, this work was soon completed. Then I turned each horse into the fold-yard for a drink out of a trough. When each horse had returned to its stall it found a second feed on its crib. Thoddy continued to feed the 6 horses and in between, groomed his pair of horses, while I groomed the remainder. After the foreman had called with his orders, we harnessed the horses for the work in hand. We had a one-hour break at noon, but there was little respite. Horses required feeding and corn bins and chaff bins had to be refilled. I carried on forking sufficient straw into the stable to bed the horses at night.

Wagoner and his waggon, Newton Garth Farm, Hedon, 1919. Hired farm-hands were noted for their conscientious concern for the horses in their care, and they almost lived in a world of their own, They imagined they owned the horses they worked, the tools they used and the ploughs they were allocated. A similar procedure was practiced with the waggons and the one claimed by the wagoner was kept in mint condition. It was never used to load muck and the wheels never turned on the land, except when the waggon was being loaded in a harvest field. The main purpose for this vehicle was to transport loads from the farm to a goods yard and "vice-versa". This imaginary ownership was most noticeable when the horsemen were at work in the stable. I experienced this and my tools were always secondhand. Should one wear out the wagoner claimed the new replacement. The foreman was smitten with the "my" bug and he couild not have been more concerned with the management of the farm had he owned it. At Martinmas he selected the workers who would be asked to 'stop again' and at the hirings he engaged the men required as replacements.

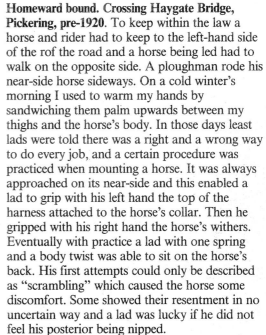

Homeward bound. Crossing Haygate Bridge, Pickering, pre-1920. To keep within the law a horse and rider had to keep to the left-hand side of the rof the road and a horse being led had to walk on the opposite side. A ploughman rode his near-side horse sideways. On a cold winter's morning I used to warm my hands by sandwiching them palm upwards between my thighs and the horse's body. In those days least lads were told there was a right and a wrong way to do every job, and a certain procedure was practiced when mounting a horse. It was always approached on its near-side and this enabled a lad to grip with his left hand the top of the harness attached to the horse's collar. Then he gripped with his right hand the horse's withers. Eventually with practice a lad with one spring and a body twist was able to sit on the horse's back. His first attempts could only be described as "scrambling" which caused the horse some discomfort. Some showed their resentment in no uncertain way and a lad was lucky if he did not feel his posterior being nipped.

A foreman, his wife and her boarders. "Abbey" took its name from the original one situated in a paddock where monks had been the first inhabitants. Alterations had been made to turn it into a dwelling-place which was occupied by the foreman, his family and the 4 hired horsemen, whose board was provided by the foreman's wife. The food if plain, was wholesome, and no different to that she served her husband who sat at the same table as we did. Mr. Bean had an agreement with the master regarding the amount of money she received monthly. She also received supply of free milk and potatoes, and permission to keep a few hens. Her husband was allowed to keep a pig and when it reached the bacon stage it was killed and the carcass cured. There were always eggs and bacon at hand. No doubt Mrs. Bean looked forward to Martinmas Day when her borders received their yearly wage and returned home to enjoy their week's holiday. Proof of the good-will she created was the number of workers who returned for another year.

A typical least-lad and his pair of plough horses, 1927. I sometimes wonder how I survived the first three years, when I was a hired farm-lad. I worked 11 hours each day, 6 days each week. This did not include stable work before and after the day's work in the field or Sunday work in winter when the horses slept in the stable. Today there is a modern iron bridge across the Derwent at Yeddingham. Also the original quaint stone bridge has been destroyed. There was passage only for one vehicle at any given time but at each side there were pockets where pedestrians could stand on fine summer evenings. Hired lads and lassies took advantage of this, including myself, a 17 year old. From this point I had a clear view of the farm where I was the wagoner's lad. Never in my wildest dreams could I have imagined the changes which were to take place. In March 1919, by law, hours of work were reduced to 9 hours from Monday to Friday and normal work finished at noon on a Saturday. There were four hired horsemen on the farm and we did not take advantage of the change until June. As could be expected there was confrontation between master and wagoner. I was not involved, so I stood by and "lapped it up".

On every landowner's estate, there were a number of small farms ideal for a "starter". It was not unusual for a foreman in middle life due mainly to his wife's industry and thrift, to save sufficient capital to lease a small farm. In the early years they had a hard struggle. If her husband could not afford extra labour at hay-time or harvest, his wife helped him in every possible way. She relieved him of the work of milking the cows and feeding the pigs and she helped in the hayfields. Harvesting was especially hard as sometimes she picked on the stack. This involved forking heavy wheat sheaves to supply the stacker. She was the last to finish working having to supply a late meal after operations ceased. During lambing time she brought the weaklings into the kitchen to the warmth of the fire and fed and kept them until they had recovered. Life became easier when her family had grown up and she received help. Readers who were children in those days will be able to recollect how hard their mothers worked.

Boxer, **the loner.** During my school days I cannot recall seeing petrol propelled vehicles, other than the local doctor's car, the brass head lamps prominent and the occasional lorry with solid tyres. It was in 1923 when I had my first ride in a motor car. It was one of the few in the Pickering area and it was owned by J. B. Armitage of Hagg House Farm. At the Hirings held at Pickering in 1920 he engaged me to be his wagoner. He practiced horse dealing and bought young horses, and when they were fully developed sold them to a buyer who supplied town firms with dray horses. Every horse on the farm was for sale at any time, except a black called *Boxer*. This big powerful shire I considered to be the most intelligent horse I had been concerned with. Every horse that was bought in was yoked for the first time on the side of *Boxer*. In the summer of 1923 J. B. bought a horse from a farmer who lived in the Whitby area and he agreed to bring the horse to the top of Blue Bank the next day. I travelled with J. B. in his car, a Ford Model T, in order to collect the horse. No doubt J. B.'s business was profitable because the following year he bought a new Citreon.

An old people's outing by waggonette in 1914. During the 1914-18 War the main mode of public transport was waggonette drawn by horses. When one was loaded to full capacity, the total weight of the passengers and vehicle out-weighed the team of horses yoked to it. Usually old and in poor condition, their mis-shaped legs gave their ages away. "Gone over the knees" was the term used. Roads were repaired with rough stones which left rough surfaces. A horse with stiff joints was liable to stumble and cut or bruise its knees. The lot of a wagonette horse was an unhappy one. If it could have talked it would have been to recall the days when it was one of a pair of carriage horses and was never subjected to harsh treatment. They were kept in a high-class stable, well fed and groomed. With the passing of the years they lost their sprightliness and were replaced by younger horses, and were sold. Those bought by town hawkers kept their horses in back street stables. They did not receive the same kind of treatment and they lost condition. Some hawkers, not content with working their horses throughout the week, yoked them to a waggonette, their passengers bound for the countryside or a resort.

A market town's station staff. The station master is seated centre, with the foreman porter and clerk. The porters stand behind. In later years when I was capable of being a waggoner, I looked upon the Wolds as God's own country. When ploughing in one particular field on Heslerton Wold in the early morning of a summer's day, I have looked across towards the moors and gazed upon a misty dew-drenched valley. After the mist had rolled away, revealed in miniature was a large area its beauty unspoilt. I could see in the distance the Scarborough to Pickering train leaving Seamer station which had the appearance of a model. As it travelled to Forge Valley the engine belched clouds of white vapour which twirled away to disappear into a blue sky. But I lost sight of the train when it left this station on its way to Wykeham until it re-appeared before entering Brompton station. When the train left this station is steamed out of my sight for good. This railway was one of the first to be scrapped under the Beeching plan. The scenes I witnessed that sunny day will never be seen again. The obsolete, deteriorating rural stations became blots on the countryside, shabby relics of the days when the railways were prosperous undertakings.

Hagg House Farm. Hagg House was recognised as one of the most productive in the area and J. B. Armitage one of the most efficient managers. The house is situated on an incline and part of the tillage lay below it. When we were at work in a field, J. B. could look-out a front window and see every move we made. In 1923 I passed my 21st birthday unrecognised. I never sent a greetings card or present, so I could not expect otherwise. But I bought a Raleigh bike for £6 and a tailor made me a suit for £5. In 1980 I returned when harvest was in full swing. I was pleased to see the little forge intact the tools still on the anvil as if a shoeing had just been completed. I made my way to the stackyard which was as bare as Mother Hubbard's cupboard. The attractive corn stacks which had once adorned it are missing for ever. Since those far off days J. B. and his family and all the men he employed have passed on.

Chapter 3
The Era of the Plough

Close-up of the fittings of a plough. The plough has always been the symbol of the countryman who was noted for ploughing a straight furrow. Before foundries came into production, ploughs were made in the village blacksmith's shop. If the beam remained intact there was no limit to the life of a plough. Towards the rear of the beam was a permanent structure known as an 'upshear'. Fixed to this was a mould board and two strakers — runners. The share covered the nose of the upshear in the same manner as a glove. The draught iron to which a cobble-tree could be attached was part of a fitting called a clevis, which was fixed to the front end of the beam. All these parts, secured with nuts and bolts, were detachable. When they became worn the blacksmith replaced them or made replacements. The wheels and coulter were held in position with clasps secured with screw bolts. The share and the coulter were the cutting parts and the mould board turned the furrows over. Although the coulter was a crude iron blade, setting it to a fraction of an inch from the point of the share was essential.

One of the last models to leave the Ransome's assembly line. The wheels controlled the width and the depth of the furrows and kept the plough on an even keel. When the share had worn, the wheels had to be adjusted if the land was to be ploughed at the correct depth. Although each blacksmith had his own design, the fittings were of a standard size. It was the custom for ploughmen to follow each other across a field and regardless of the different makes, it was possible for ploughmen to set their ploughs to turn over identical furrows. This was very important when a seed bed was being created.

Ploughing in line, Wold Farm, West Heslerton, in 1925. There was an improvement in the design of ploughs when factories came into production. New style clasps made it more convenient to adjust the wheels. Ransome's turned out the largest and heaviest, ideal for ploughing strong land and I used one at Rise Carr Farm. My favourite was a Hornsby plough similar in design as a Ransome, but not as heavy.

A "double-decker" at work in 1918. One afternoon in March 1918 I was ploughing with a double furrow plough drawn by three horses. Although the sun was shining there was a nip in the air, a warning of frost. I was ploughing uphill and when I came to the end of the furrow I could see a weasel and a rabbit on the herdland. The latter was paralysed with fear as its enemy encircled it. Eventually the weasel was able to jump on to the rabbit's back and bite deep into its neck and suck its blood. The weasel was so engrossed wuith its prey it had not noticed the horses approach. So I decided to kill it. Carried on the plough was a small iron plate — blacksmith made — which I used to remove soil which had stuck on the wheels and other parts of the plough. I picked this up to use as a weapon, but after I had taken two paces the weasel jumped off the rabbit's back and disappeared in the hedge bottom. Such an incident concerned with nature will not be witnessed again on this farm. The land is now barren of trees and hedges. Birds have lost cover for their nests and small field animals their hiding places in the hedge bottoms. Many species of insects and flowers have become extinct.

Ploughing with three horses on the Wolds in 1920. During the depression which followed the 1914-18 War many Wold farmers turned to "double deckers" to save labour and costs. A waggoner with one of these ploughs drawn by three horses could turn over as many furrows in a day as two men, each with a pair of horses.

At work with a Holderness plough, 1920. Before man acquired the knowledge and skill to weld iron, ploughs were completely made of wood. Several years ago one was found on a farm in Holderness. In this area after iron ploughs came onto the market, the beams and handles were made of wood until horse ploughs became obsolete. No doubt ploughmen appreciated iron fittings when they became available. A village joiner and blacksmith worked in conjunction when making a Holderness plough, and according to tradition, when a farmer required a new one he sent his wagoner to the joiner to be measured to ensure the handles were the correct height. Holderness is noted for its clay sub-soil, yet good crops are produced. Today with the use of modern machines, ploughing or cultivation is no problem. This was not always the case when horses were a farmer's only power.

Bush Farm. Holderness, pre-1920. Ploughing a stubble field in particular was a hard slog. It was not unusual to see three or perhaps four horses yoked to a plough controlled by the lone ploughman. The horses worked in harmony and they pulled the plough at a regular, steady gate across the field throughout the day. When a young horse was being schooled to work, it was trained to turn clock-wise at the words *Gee-back* and likewise the opposite way to the words *Warv up*. A horse never forgot these commands which were essential to a ploughman when turning his team on the headland. A field scheduled to produce roots was ploughed across the existing furrows which broke up into large clots.

Turning clots over with a digger plough minus wheels. Further ploughing was impossible unless the wheels were removed and this operation was referred to as swing ploughing. Skill was required to turn over furrows the correct width and depth. 'Open clots' tested a lad's ability to handle a team of horses. Care had to be taken when turning them on the headland. Should one stumble and its shoe make contact with its partner's leg, most likely the skin would be cut and blood would appear. It was the youngest and the old horses which suffered the most. The former had not learned to pick across the field and they were the most difficult to turn on the headlands. The old horses, perhaps the result of rheumatism, had lost their sprightliness and were likely to stumble over the largest clots. It was these conditions which were responsible for horses being lathered with sweat when the sun was blazing down. Ploughmen suffered in this respect too.

Swing ploughing on a farm in Holderness, 1923. A Wold wagoner when ploughing never experienced such uncomfortable conditions, or drove a team of horses in the same manner as a Holderness ploughman. Using a check rein and a false line, the near-side horse was coupled to its partner. Attached to its bit were a pair of short reins which passed over the horse's collar and between the harness. Connected to the reins was a plough string of sufficient length to reach the handle on the plough and complete the check rein. The false line, a broad rein, was laid across the far side of the horse's back. Two small chains fixed to one end of the false line were attached to the horse's bit rings. A single chain connected the other end to its partner's trace. This did not apply to me. My horses were coupled together and I drove them with a pair of strings, each attached to the horses' respective bits.

Ploughing in line, 1919. I considered December to be the most miserable month for a horseman. There were gloomy days and adverse weather conditions. When ploughing was in progress we only saw the farmstead in daylight an hour at noon. In a morning it was dark when the pairs of horses left the stables and no lamps were carried. It was a ghost procession. The only sounds heard were the clip-clop of horses feet and the jingle of traces. On arrival at the field we 'yoked up' in the dark and often plough wheels were turning before the dawn. Ploughing continued into the afternoon until the evening shadows began to fall. The foreman was satisfied if ploughing the stubble field was completed in December. In the new year it was the turn of the clover fields which had provided pastures for the sheep the previous summer. This was ploughing at its best and furrow ridges without a break in each one could be seen the length of the field. A wagoner ensured every furrow was plumb straight and it was possible to plough an acre in a day to a depth of 4 inches, the furrows 8 inches wide.

One of the first pre-1850 threshing machines. The large workforce was required to carry sheaves from a stack. Due to the dust created, threshing corn was the only work on a horse farm which could be considered as unhealthy On a windy day the dust penetrated into a man's nose; it affected his eyes and also coated his lips, colouring them black.

The phrase 'threshing corn' originated in the distant past when the grain was separated from the ears by threshing or beating with a 'flail'. This was a wooden instrument: a staff which had been swingle-hinged to a handle.

Progress was made during the early ears of the 19th century when a threshing machine was invented. It was static and positioned in a barn where corn sheaves were stored. Power to drive it was provided by a horse wheel which was connected to the machine with a cam-shaft. Three short poles were fixed to the wheel and a horse was yoked to each one. When they pulled as they walked in a circle, the wheel turned and set the threshing machine in motion. The wheel was housed in a round shed and between the top of the walls and the roof was an opening. The fresh air which passed through the shed benefited the horses.

One of the first portable engines in operation.
During the second half of the 19th century, more land came under cultivation and increased corn production was the result. The sheaves were built into stacks and a mobile threshing machine, which would be placed near each stack, was essential. The advent of steam solved the problem.

The first steam engine used to power a threshing machine was mounted on four wooden wheels. Fixed to the forward end of the frame was a turntable. Attached to it was a pair of shafts to which a horse could be yoked. It was called a portable engine and when a machine was mounted on wheels in a similar manner a 'threshing set' was formed.

Threshing machine and portable engine on the move. The owner of a 'set' provided a service for the farmers living in a certain area. When one required this service, it was his responsibility to bring the set to that farm from wherever it had been in operation. Two teams of horses were sent and the number in each one depended on the condition of the roads. On the Yorkshire Wolds, where there were hills to climb, each team consisted of four horses.

Threshing took place during the winter months. It was often dark when the wagoners arrived with the engine and machine, and with the aid of stable lamps they were sited near the stack to be threshed.

The official speed for an engine travelling on the open road was 4 miles per hour, reduced to 3 when the set was passing through a village. The hiring rate for a threshing set was £1 per day. The farmer concerned provided the crew with 3 meals, as well as coal and water for the engine. Due to the travelling time, it was not unusual for the crew to work a 12 hour day.

In 1873, a traction engine was designed and built. It could travel under its own steam and also tow a threshing machine. It was near the end of the century before portable engines were completely replaced.

It was now the owner's responsibility to transport his 'set' to the farm where it was required. Perhaps he would be a village tradesman who had a flair for machinery. He employed two men: an engine driver who was the one in authority and was responsible for any breakdowns or delays and the feeder who fed the sheaves into the machine. He also steered the engine when travelling between farms.

Threshing at Hagg House Farm, c.1925. After a day's threshing had been completed, the machine was swept down, the hatches closed and then covered with a tarpaulin sheet ready for the journey to the next farm. On arrival, the engine and machine were positioned near a corn stack. The same procedure as practised in the past. After the crew had eaten the suppers provided, they returned home. They arrived early the next morning in order to steam the engine and prepare the machine — oil the bearings etc. — before sitting down to breakfast with the hired workers.

Threshing at Thornton Dale in the 1920s. Note the dog guarding the lunch basket. A workforce of 10 was required. 2 men forked the sheaves from the stack into the machine, 2 carried the grain in sacks into the granary, 3 carried the straw from the machine to a site where a fourth man stacked it. The two youngest hired hands carried the chaff into a building.

The sheets used for this purpose were made of hessian and measured 5 feet square. No doubt carrying chaff was the most unpleasant task experienced on a threshing day. It was collected onto a sheet by using a wooden rake. A lad had to work in a confined space between the machine and the stack. To add to his discomfort loose corn fell off the machine onto him and a sore neck might be the result. When a lad carrying a full sheet of chaff was walking away from the machine, all that could be seen of his back view were his cap, his legs below his knees, and his boots.

When elevators became available, straw carriers were no longer required. The 3 men who carried the straw were known as 'Straw Jackers' and the forks they used were referred to as a 'Straw Jacks'. The two tines fixed to the handle were each a foot long and the width between them six inches. A certain amount of skill was required and some men became noted for their ability to carry straw. As the straw dropped from the machine, it was packed in a certain manner to form a firm unit. The fork was then plunged into it and carried in an upright position. The handle was pressed against the carrier's shoulder and the end of the handle held in the palm of his hand. When the stack gained height, the straw was carried up a ladder in this manner. Sheaves were dropped into a machine in an upright position and minimum damage was done to the straw. This was not noticeable in wheat straw which retained its firm straight condition.

Threshing at the Grange, 1920. There were sufficient hands on a large farm to man a 'threshing set', but a small farmer had to engage casual workers. Men known as 'tramp threshers' followed the set from one farm to another. In the 1920s the rate was 10 shillings per day, 1 shilling extra for the corn carriers. Fork lifts and similar machines have taken most of the hard work out of farming and no longer have men to lift or carry heavy sacks.

The combines too have taken the hard work out of harvesting and, better still, made the threshing machines obsolete. No-one regrets the passing of the 'threshing sets'. Farm workers are well rid of the dirt, dust and hard work which was involved. One of the most pleasant scenes witnessed in those days was a traction engine towing a machine out of the stackyard away from the farm.

Sheeted-down, and ready to move on to the next farm. One of the first farm tractors to be operated in the 1920s was called a *Titon*. In appearance it could be described as comical when compared to the modern one. Fixed to it was a pulley and sufficient energy could be generated to power a threshing machine. The fuel required was paraffin and was cheaper than coal, and the tractor could be serviced in a matter of minutes. It did not need constant attention throughout the day and there was no need for a man to rise early in order to get steam up as was the case with a traction engine.

An early Titan tractor. A *Titan* tractor had one disadvantage. Although it could tow a machine on level roads, there were problems when the ground was soft. It was not unusual while threshing was in progress to see the wheels on the machine sink below the fellies. When this happened, a team of horses was yoked to the machine in order to pull it onto a hard surface.

A waggon drawn by a pair of Clydesdale horses, which were not as heavy as Shires. The derelict rural railway tracks and stations are an addition to a deteriorating countryside; yet there was a period when they contributed to its beauty. The rails, which gleamed in the sun, and tracks were well maintained and kept free from weeds. Before motor transport became established, all farmers' grain and stock which had to travel outside the district was sent by rail from the nearest station. Any requirements a farmer did not buy locally, came by rail and he bought his coal via the station master. Farmers' waggons travelling to and from the goods yards in the winter were a common sight on country roads.

During this period extra feeding stuffs were required to feed stock which were kept in buildings. After a threshing day the sold grain was delivered to the goods yard for despatch. There were no mechanical lifts and sacks containing wheat (18 stones), barley (16 stones), and oats (12 stones) were man-handled from a waggon into a railway truck. When an extra 'lift' was required wagoners and porters helped each other. I can recall after delivering a load of grain to Pocklington station and was homeward bound, my horses stopped on their own accord at the *Cross Keys* — a habit practiced by the previous wagoner, and the horses remembered!

This waggon loaded with 30 sacks of barley was photographed in 1920 as it passed through South Dalton on the road to Kiplincoates station. On the top of the granary steps was a stone platform and a waggon was loaded from this point. The sacks were handed down to a wagoner who placed them in three sections, each one containing 10 sacks. Two were laid in the waggon body, their mouths pointing to the rear. The next sack was placed on the top and centre of the two. Then a sack was laid at each end on the shelvings, the seams pointing outwards. Three more sacks followed and these fitted snugly between the previous three. Two more sacks completed the section, and two more of the latter completed the load but the mouths of the sacks were pointing to the front. Regardless of the road surface on which the waggon travelled, a safe load could be guaranteed if the sacks were loaded in this manner. On the Wolds where there were hills to climb, four horses were required to pull a waggon loaded with 30 sacks, total weight 3 tons.

Typical Wold waggon. All the waggons had poles attached to them and when four horses were yoked to one in tandem a wagoner road the near-side pole horses, referred to as the saddle horse, and from this position drove the leading pair. It was a more pleasant experience driving them uphill, because there were no brakes as such. The near-side wheel was fitted over a small iron sledge called a shoe, which was connected to the waggon body with a strong chain. When the summit was reached, a halt was made and the shoe placed in position. When the waggon was restarted, the wheel lodged on the shoe, then there was another stoppage while a lock chain was attached to the wheel between two spokes, As a safety measure, should the shoe give way the wheel was held stationary. The two pole horses were as well trained as circus animals. If a waggon gained speed they literally sat in their breechings to steady it on a slippery road. I used to steer the waggon to the near-side of the road which enabled the shoe which had lost its grip to bite into the grass verge. The two chains fixed to the end of the pole and hooked onto the horses' harnesses were subjected to a heavy strain.

A Wold transport unit from Welton Wold in the 1920s. Without breechings the collars would have been pulled onto the horses' necks. A breeching was a length of reinforced leather, three inches wide which passed round a horse's hind-quarters between its hocks and rump. It was connected to the horse's harness by two chains and held in position with quarter straps buckled to the horse's collar. This breaking system was a precarious affair, and if it had failed the waggon would have over-run the horses. Among the entanglement of frightened, maimed horses would have been the remains of a wagoner!

This photo illustrates the position of the breechings and their connection to the horse collars. During the 1914-18 War, due to the hostilities at sea, many provisions were in short supply, none more so than sugar. When the government became aware sugar was being extracted from sugar beet in France, British farmers were encouraged to grow crops. The roots were so deep-rooted, before they could be lifted it was necessary to disturb them. A plough was specially designed for this purpose, and a pair of powerful horses yoked to it was the best bet. When the roots had been harvested they were despatched from the nearest station. In order to increase the capacity of a waggon, side boards and end boards were attached to it.

A Foden steam waggon. When the iron-ore mines were in production at Rosedale, situated on the North Yorkshire Moors, their tall chimneys could be seen from a wide area. A Malton brewery supplied the beer for the thirsty miners. The barrels were conveyed on a waggon drawn by 6 horses. After they had passed through Pickering the horses faced a long haul uphill. During the first decade of this century the waggon was replaced with a Foden steam waggon. Getting a horse or a team to pass it was a test for the best of wagoners, as I realised through my own experiences. My first encounter occurred during the summer of 1916, when I was driving *Jess* yoked to the trap on the Malton road towards Pickering. When the steam waggon came into view, the frightened mare turned the trap round immediately and would have galloped home if I had lost control. On my second attempt I ensured *Jess* did not play this trick a second time. The vehicle was stationary and help was at hand from the driver and his mate. Each one grabbed a rein attached to the mare's bit and then led her past. I continued my journey to Pickering

A good illustration of how three horses were yoked to a waggon. Eight years later when I was the wagoner at Hagg House Farm, I experienced my second encounter with a Foden waggon. I was returning from Pickering driving 3 horses yoked to a waggon with a load of cattle cakes. A single horse in the lead has more freedom than a pair coupled together, otherwise the following incident might not have happened. The Foden waggon approaching was literally crawling along and the horses showed no signs of nervousness. Suddenly the lead horse turned into the path of the vehicle, unusual and certainly not expected. It was stopped instantly and the driver and his mate soon had the horse under control. After they had led it past, the driver said 'if we hadn't been going dead slow we would have run over the horse'. The horse in question *Royal* was a powerful Shire, the ideal dray horse. Soon after the incident with the steam-waggon, he was sold to a dealer who supplied the railway stables in York. The horse was on trial for a month and if he had been unmanageable among traffic he would have been returned. The first time *Royal* saw a tram he squatted on the road in a similar manner as a rabbit. The promise of £1 from the dealer persuaded the driver to persevere with the horse and to my disappointment he was not returned.

continued from page 40

station to meet my grandfather who had spent a week with my aunt at Wykeham. On our return he held the reins and I decided not to tell him of the mare's antics otherwise he may have tickled *Jess* on her rump with his whip.

On the road to a field with a load of manure. The weather was then more seasonable than it is today and in January we expected frosts and snow which tempered the land. The benefit from this was seen in the spring, when cultivation was in progress to create seed beds. When ploughing was held up there was plenty of other work to do. The Foreman visited each stable before breakfast and left his orders. After a keen frost we were not surprised to hear him say 'Gear yer 'osses to plug muck', which meant leading manure from the fold yard to a field where it was contained in a 'middin'. Waggon or cart wheels made little imprint on the land when it was frozen. Otherwise at the time of the year the wheels would have sunk in. On a small farm carts were used, each one drawn by two horses yoked tandem fashion. The 'first 'oss' was driven by word of mouth.

Leading manure from a fold-yard at Keyingham in the 1920s. The manure was contained in a 'middin' which was made square and compact. The manure was not distibured again until the summer when cultivation was in progress. During this delay the straw among the manure perished and also any weed seeds.

Returning from a field with the cart empty, Far Barr Farm, Hedon, 1911. A continuous supply of turnip was required to feed cattle, and hail, rain, snow or blow these were carted from field to farm. When passing through a village I was not surprised when a woman standing on her door-step shouted "Drop us a tonup off lad", and I duly obliged. A cart required less horse-power than a waggon mounted on four wheels, yet two horses were required to pull a loaded cart out of a field when the land was soft. Over the years the horse yoked between the shafts had developed the knack of steering or reversing the cart without undue effort. I have experienced loading a cart in the middle of a field in a snowstorm. I covered each horse's back with a sack. No doubt they were as pleased as I was when the load was completed and we could wend our way home.

Typical farm cart in the 1920s, with the horse properly yoked. It was essential for the comfort of the horse to adjust the harness to fit the respective parts of its body. The shafts had to be raised to be on par with the horse's shoulders and breeching chains. If the shafts were raised above this level the shoulder chains became taut and pressure was put on the horse's back. The reverse had the opposite effect and the shafts were continually jogging up and down when the cart was in motion. The length of the breeching chains which allowed the horse freedom of movement were adjusted when it was required to back the cart. The position of a load was important too. It had to be evenly balanced, not too heavy or too light. This knowledge could only be acquired through experience.

43

Carting sheaves home, in the true sense of the word. On the Yorkshire Moors the majority of the farms were family affairs; otherwise many farmers would not have remained solvent if it had been necessary to employ outside labour. There were hills and dales to contend with and carts were the best mode of transport.

A wagoner taking part in a horse-driving competition, July 1913. This is an unusual photograph. It is difficult to assume correctly the occasion and the activities taking place. The wagoner is not wearing his working clothes and there is little to suggest a show is being held. There are no reins attached to the respective horses' bit rings, but between their heads can be seen part of a riding saddle, attached to the near-side horse. After Sir Mark Sykes formed his band of Wagoner Reserves, driving trials were held in which each wagoner rode his near-side horse army-fashion, and no doubt this is the answer.

Three horses yoked to a muck waggon. In an exceptionally dry summer it was not unusual for drinking water to be in short supply and it was obtained from the nearest village. I experienced this in 1925 when the well dried up at Hagg House. A supply was obtained from Thornton le Dale and only *Boxer* the black horse could pull a full cart up the hill out of the village to the farm. The cart was joiner-made. An 18 gallon ex-spirit barrel was fixed to a frame mounted on two wheels with a pair of shafts attached. Many Wold farmers had to rely on a pond to satisfy stock and this was sited at the bottom of a hill and water seeped into it. Waggons were favoured on the Wold farms and three horses were required to pull one carrying a load of manure. This was an opportunity to yoke a young horse to a waggon for the first time.

Loading water from the village pump for household use at Seaton early in the century. In the summer, water was conveyed in the cart to pastures and this was the least lad's job. The horse backed the cart into the pond to a depth of about 3 feet, and then the lad turned it round in order to have a straight pull out of the pond. He filled the cart with a small container fixed to fork shafts and in doing so he had to stand with his back to the horse and keep an eye on it. After a hot day's work in a fallow field the horses loved to stand in a pond while they were drinking their fill.

In the summer it was not unusual to see a smith at work outside his forge. The village streets were quiet and peaceful before motor transport took control of the roads. One sound frequently heard throughout the day was the ring of the blacksmith's hammer. His services to the local farmers were essential — a man of many parts — and there was no end to his ability. He ensured all implements were kept in working order. Harrows with stunted teeth propped up against the outside wall of his shop were a sign spring was near —when they would be required to form a seed bed. A blacksmith also made hooks and loops, fittings for swingle trees and cobble-trees, crooks and hinges for field gates. He made the fittings for waggons and carts built by the village joiner and they often worked together when hooping the wheels of a waggon. All this work went by the board when a wagoner arrived with a pair of horses requiring new shoes, a privilege every horseman had and a welcome change from the regular routine of the farm. The Foreman made the final selection and more than one lad would inform him with a ride to the forge in mind "it's tarm my 'osses was shod, boss". On a wet morning when ploughing was held up a smith could expect to see a number of horses standing outside his shop.

The forge at Anlaby with a typical village blacksmith. The recruiting poster on the notice-board dates the photo to the 1914-1918 War.
Without shoes horses became foot-sore and eventually lame. Shoeing was highly skilled work. A smith was noted for his craftsmanship and his ability to handle horses. The latter stood him in good stead when fixing a young horse's first set of shoes. Patience was required when shoeing its hind feet and a twitch on the horse's nose was used only as a last resort. Some of the most difficult to shoe were the older horses. With stiffness in their joints they were inclined to put weight on the smith, when nailing a hind shoe on. Before the 1914-18 War smiths made the horses' shoes, but in later years ready-made ones could be bought. Care was taken when hammering the nails in to avoid pricking the tender part of a horse's foot. The nails were in a neat straight line and when the hooves had been rasped smooth they had a new look too. The new set of shoes made a resounding noise as the horse walked out of the cobbled floor of the shop into the village street. I used to enjoy this pleasant interlude in the blacksmith's shop, pumping the bellow while I watched the smith at work. This was not possible on a farm with its own forge. A jobbing smith would visit the farm when the horses required new shoes.

Chapter 6
Spring Sowing

Harrowing in a field at King Thorpe farm above Pickering. Some farmers would not allow corn to be sown before March, but I have drilled oats in February when the weather was favourable. It was essential to complete sowing in the shortest possible time. In March the farmstead was alive with animals. Lambing time was in full swing and the mares were producing their foals. The horses were looking their best, their ribs well covered with flesh. They had cast their winter coats and their skins gleamed in the spring sunshine. This was the result of the care and attention the horses had received during the winter months. The three-year olds had filled out and were now able to work on the side of older partners. A team trailed a set of harrows across a field at a regular steady gate, and only stopped when it was necessary. The horses' rations of oats were increased from a stone each day to one-and-a-half. In the morning stable work began an hour earlier to ensure the horses' bellies were full.

At work breaking down the clots with a Cambridge roller, Wold farm, West Heslerton, 1925.
I considered more knowledge was required to cultivate the land with horses, when compared to operating a machine. If there is no mechanical fault a tractor can be operated for any length of time in one session, and there is sufficient power to tow an implement regardless of its weight or size. Horses, being flesh and blood, were subjected to hunger, thirst and tiredness. Therefore they could only be worked a limited number of hours in one spell. If instead of three horses, two had been yoked to a set of three harrows they would soon have become exhausted. The state of the land had to be taken into consideration too. A pair of horses could pull a Cambridge roller when the clots were small; otherwise three or perhaps four would be required. When I was a wagoner's lad and my horses showed signs of distress, I complained and another was added to my team.

Drilling corn, with a lad leading the first horses, the wagoner leading the drill horse, and the Foreman following the drill. Oats were sown on land which had previously grown clover and had been ploughed in February. As soon as the sheep had eaten off a crop of turnips, the land was ploughed, two inches deep to enable the barley crop which followed to obtain the best results from the sheeps' manure. The corn drills made in the 19th century were heavy and cumbersome, and three horses were required to pull one and three hands to operate it. The seed dropped down the 11 spouts and each one fitted into a coulter. This parted the seed bed and created a row for the seed to drop into, covering it in the process. In the seed box was a revolving spindle and the power was provided by two connected cog wheels. One was attached to the spindle and the other to the far-side travelling wheel. To disengage the cog wheels the seed box was jacked up with a lever held in position by a clip. A chain connected each coulter to a roller fixed across the drill and when this was turned the coulters were raised from the ground. It was by these means the Foreman was able to neutralize the drill, before it was turned round on the headland.

Driving a fine pair of horses yoked to a drill on a fine spring day was a pleasure. After the 1914-18 War an all-metal drill, except for the seed box and pole, appeared on the market. Two horses could pull, one yoked at each side of the pole. Drilling corn was a wagoner's responsibility and it was no mean feat driving a pair of horses and keeping an eye on the coulters. Should one become blocked with soil unnoticed until the spout overflowed, there was a missing row until the harvest. Attached to the end of the pole was a short wooden bar which was strapped to each horse's respective collar and they and the drill became one. I chose a pair of horses with a good walking action. If one was inclined to 'roll' the drill was pulled out of line and a wide row could have been the result. Before farm workers received paid holidays, I drilled many an acre on Good Friday and Easter Monday.

This photograph of horses with a corn-seed drill was taken in 1950 on Trinity House Farm, Swanland, a scene unlikely to be witnessed again. Finding horses of such a high standard trained to work on the land would be a problem. The drill was one of the last to be made in the Hornsby factory and two powerful horses were required. Driving them to a mark from behind the drill is the reason Mr. Chambers, the tenant farmer, is out of sight. His son is pictured driving the horse yoked to a set of light harrows.

Following a seed-drill with a set of light harrows, 1920. When drilling was in progress a lad, driving a pair of horses, yoked to a set of light harrows with straight teeth, followed the drill to cover the seed. When a field was completed there were no foot marks to be seen either the lad's or the horses. The headlands were the last to be harrowed and when this work was completed the horses were unyoked outside the gate while the harrows remained inside the field.

Drilling seed corn on Wold Farm, West Heslerton in 1920s. The grey mare was in foal. Hares do not create a special place to have their young. They are born in March close to a hedge, in a grass field off the beaten track. The small leverets are forsaken at an early age. At this time of the year the fields sown with winter wheat were well covered and the young hares hid among the corn until they had developed their long legs to enable them to run quickly when danger threatened. April was the month when wheat was harrowed to break the hard crust which had formed between the rows. It was important not to disturb the roots and light harrows with straight teeth were used for this purpose. While this work was in progress, the leverets' lives were in danger. Many owed their survival to the sharp eyes of horsemen who removed them from the path of their teams. While spring corn was being sown peewits were laying their eggs in the fallows scheduled to be sown with turnip seeds. A nest was a crude affair, a few stubble straws placed in a depression such as a horse's footing. In each one four eggs were laid the narrow ends pointing to middle. When a start was made to cultivate a fallow field the birds flew in the vicinity of their nests and they were not difficult to find. As was the case with the leverets the eggs were removed from the path of the horses.

At Rise Car Farm in 1916, *Blossom* is yoked between the shafts, while *Jess*, the mare in traces, is in foal. After lambing time was completed the shepherd moved his flock from a home pasture to a young clover field. We got rid of the ewes melancholy lamentations and the bleetings of the lambs when they had lost sight of their mothers. In April *Daisy* and *Blossom* produced their foals, special in my eyes. When a mare's first became noticeable she was never yoked in the middle of a three-horse team or this may have caused her some discomfort. A mare in this state was never yoked to a pair of shafts attached to a vehicle. The strain of reversing one loaded, and the tight breeching which encircled her hind quarters could have been fatal to the foal she was carrying. It was possible for a mare heavy in foal to lay down in a stall and become wedged. The effect of freeing her and lifting her on to her feet might result in a dead foal being produced. To avoid this happening the mare slept in a loose box. I can recall how jealous *Daisy* was of her foal the first few days. She gnashed her teeth when I entered the loose box.

When this Shire mare *Blossom* had her first foal, I was the wagoner's lad at Abbey Farm in 1919. A mare usually foaled during the night and if she did not require help, you were lucky if you caught her. When a mare had been due to foal, I used to 'cat nap' in the kitchen during the night and visit the loose box every hour, and even then she eluded me. Yet I was always pleased to see a mare lying peaceful and her foal standing near her. *Daisy* was so jealous of her foal the first few days she bared her teeth when I entered the loose box. During this period I mixed a bran mash among her feeds and gave her 'luke warm' water to drink. When a mare was ready for work again she was fed, groomed and harnessed in the stable. *Daisy* often tried my patience. She was anxious when she had to leave her foal while she was working. She was restless when I was unyoking her at noon and I had to hold her in check with a tight rein on our way home. On arrival at the fold yard there was bedlam while I stripped the mare. The two animals whinnied to each other and the foal rattled the door of the box with its front feet. When they came together the only sounds heard were those created when the mare was feeding and the foal suckling.

This photograph which features a chestnut Shire mare and her foal — their white legs matching, would be difficult to capture on film today. The pattern of the mare's rib cage is plain to see, but there is a reason for this. After her foal was born the first week in April, she had become one of a team of three horses. She had worked through the summer when fallows were under cultivation and also suckled her foal and this had taken its toll. It was now July and the last field had been sown with turnip, and she could take a well earned rest until the harvest. During this time her condition would improve until once again her rib cage would be out of sight.

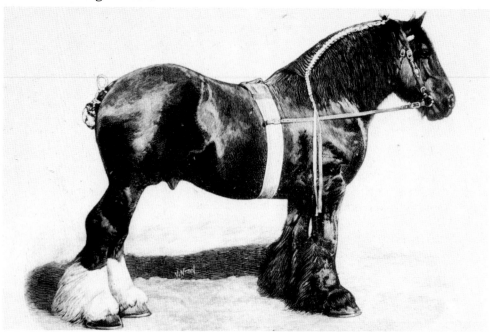

***Hendre Champion*, winner at the London Shire Horse Show**. At the turn of the century the Shire horse population was at its peak and the breeding had reached a high standard. The stallions stood no less than 14 hands, in weight less than a ton and they dwarfed a groom of average size. The winner at the London Shire Horse Show was recognised as the supreme champion. The stallion named *Hendre Champion* won this award in 1901, 1902 and 1903 and was sold for a record price of 4,100 guineas.

***Stanton House King*.** This stallion was a winner of many prizes at Shire Horse Shows. In 1908 for a figure of 3000 guineas, it was sold to Mr. Lindley of Sheepridge, Huddersfield. It would be impossible to find today a stallion similar in build and weight.

Eaton Friar Prince **was owned by the Duke of Westminster and came seventh in the London Shire Horse Show in 1924**. Before the year 1920 the principal mode of road transport was horse-drawn vehicles, all goods, food etc. being delivered in this manner. It is true to say the railways could not have functioned without the services of the heavy horses. They required the powerful shires to shunt waggons in marshalling yards and into sidings. All goods carted to and from goods yards were conveyed on horse-drawn vehicles. On many landowners' estates there was a stud farm where only pure bred stock were kept, and each horse's number and pedigree recorded. The best colt foals were retained as stallions and when three years old were ready for service. In Yorkshire the two most popular breeds were the Shires and Clydesdales.

Lord Stewart. The Shires were the heaviest and most powerful with broad quarters, heavy bones and strong joints. The horses' shoulders were of a similar depth as the length of its front legs. A gelding when yoked to a dray could pull one carrying a load weighing up to 3 tons. The Clydesdale was a different type, with longer legs, finer bones and smaller bellies. Although not as powerful as the Shires, they could travel faster and were ideal for delivering goods in a town. The supply of dray horses came from the farms where they were bred, reared and broken in when 2 years of age, and schooled to work a year later.

Burscough Friar, **a five-year old Shire stallion, the property of the Duke of Westminster.** The mating season, or travelling season as it was better known, began on April 1st and continued until the end of June. During this period a stallion was available to every farmer in the country. In the previous month, March, a groom travelled a stallion round an allocated district and paid a courtesy visit to each farmer to enable him to view the horse. If it was suitable for requirements a farmer would inform the groom the number of mares he would require the stallion to serve. When a groom had acquired a specified number of mares, this would be his round for the season. Many grooms with their charges left their bases on a Monday morning and did not return until the following Saturday, staying each night at pre-arranged lodgings. Elderly grooms were provided with a pony to ride, but the majority walked at the side of their stallions.

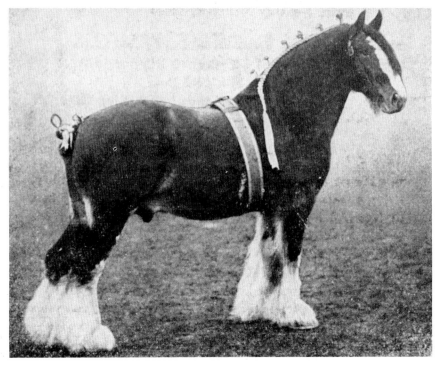

Each groom was issued with a stud card which he handed out to his customers.

58

***Chanticleer IV*, a black five-year old Shire stallion, the property of the Duke of Westminster**. In the village where I attended school there was a stud farm and the head groom was Mr. Bowman who was highly respected. He had travelled stallions for over 30 years, and on my way to school I used to meet Mr. Bowman starting out on his rounds. When the stallion was passing a field where mares were at work, I could hear its piercing cry before it came into sight. One stallion, which he travelled, a chestnut, had a silver mane and tail. The old man claimed it was the best Mr. Bowman had travelled, but it had a vicious temper. In later years when its off-spring had developed and had been schooled to work, they were not difficult to recognise. The wagoner's pair at Elm Tree Farm had been sired by the chestnut stallion. Their colour and fine carriage were similar and they had inherited its vicious temper. One Martinmas a wagoner who was a local preacher only stayed a month. His excuse was "No man cud, sarve God, an drarv them two osses".

This pure bred Shire mare gained the highest award in her class at the London Shire Horse Show in 1902. The tenant farmers on the Kirby Misperton estate were noted for their outstanding Shire horses and John Wilson, the tenant of Home Farm, could take credit for this. He was a noted dealer and he supplied the railway stables in Hull with dray horses. He would only consider buying five-year old geldings, but if he came across a young mare, an extra fine specimen, he would buy it knowing there would be a demand for it from his fellow tenants. Breeding dray horses was a profitable business. There was the cost of a horse's fodder until it had been schooled to work, then it earned its keep and each year its value increased. When farms became completely mechanised, horse-drawn vehicles became obsolete and the days of the travelling stallions passed, never to return.

An L.N.E.R. dray, once a common sight on the streets of Hull. When motor haulage companies became established in the late 1920s goods were transported direct by road and the railways lost their monopoly of long distance freight. The decline of the railways affected the number of horses that were required. In 1939 those kept in the Hull stables had been reduced from 470 to less than 300. During this decade motor vehicles had come to the fore in towns. The drayman and his horse were on their way out. The position was reversed during the war which followed, when petrol was rationed. Motor vehicles were laid up and draymen brought out of retirement. Once again horses played a part in the war effort. Thankfully they were not sent to the front line to suffer cruelty and death, as was the case in the First World War. After peace was declared, factories which had produced munitions reverted to the manufacture of motor vehicles to suit all conveyances. Eventually the horses' usefulness came to an end. They were slaughtered wholesale regardless of age or condition, and their carcasses processed into pet food. A sad end to animals which had given such good service to mankind. All who had been involved throughout their working lives with horses were surprised and shocked at the speed they disappeared from the streets.

Chapter 8
Summer Fallows

Early morning collection in a pasture, 1920.

The total area under crops and grass in the East Riding of Yorkshire. In 1930 there were 662,447 acres under crops and grass, of which 630,823 were arable. In 1937 the figures were 656,259 and 418,064. The cropping was as follows:

	1930			1937	
Wheat	70,671	acres	Wheat	92,199	acres
Barley	51,962	"	Barley	45,407	"
Oats	86,252	"	Oats	68,453	"
Potatoes	11,395	"	Potatoes	12,387	"
Sugar Beet	9,194	"	Sugar Beet	12,686	"
Carrots	1,589	"	Carrots	2,648	"

Animals substained on farms

	1930		1937
Cattle	91,610	Cattle	106,910
Sheep	400,136	Sheep	397,142
Pigs	68,999	Pigs	122,127
Horses	28,764	Horses	26,795

On days when a full complement of horses were not required, it was the mares with foals at foot which were rested. In April the young corn crops were gradually covering the brown earth and once again the pastures were flushed with grass. Soon it would be 'turning out time' when the horses would feed and gallop in the pastures throughout the summer. This order from the Foreman was always welcome "if it's a fine weekend, tunn yer osses out". On the first occasion the horses realised their freedom, the youngest galloped away from the gate and showed us a clean pair of heels. The mares stayed and rolled on their backs from side to side, sampling the luscious grass. The mares were turned into a separate pasture which was strange territory to their foals. Each one galloped round its mother several times before nibbling at the grass. After being tied down to horse keeping from the previous October, free weekends and evenings were appreciated. But every weekday morning the horses had to be brought from the pastures into the stable where they were groomed and harnessed for the work in hand before breakfast. Previously, when the horses had slept in the stable, a 5 a.m. start was made to prepare them. This extra hour in bed was welcome. It was the oldest horses which were the most difficult to catch and they had to be coaxed with a piece of linseed cake. I enjoyed these early morning walks, the exercise and the effort involved preparing the horses for work stimulated my appetite.

A Cambridge roller at work. Notice the discs which bit into clots. When the last field of barley had been sown, cultivation of the fallows followed until the end of June. Men and horses were subjected to boring and hard work. There was little interest in following a team yoked to an implement across a field. In the early stages there might be clots to hop over too. The fields which had been ploughed in the previous December were 'quartered', ploughed across the existing furrows which disintegrated. Alternate dragging and rolling followed. The former disturbed the clots and the latter crushed them. The weeds were separated in the process. Cultivation continued until it was possible to create a seed bed. The seed was so small and very fine tilth was necessary, or the young shoot would not have been able to break through. The Cambridge roller was a collection of discs fixed to a frame with a pole attached and the number of horses required to pull it depended on the size of the clots. The only drag I worked with had been made in a blacksmith's shop. It consisted of an oblong iron frame and attached to it were a number of long chisel teeth harrows. The frame was mounted on two wheels, and at the front two pieces of angle iron formed a triangle and at this point was the draw hook. Three horses could pull the drag, and it was rough walking for their driver.

Leading manure from a midden to scatter on the land. At this stage rain would be welcome to settle the dust and cool the atmosphere. Operations were held up until the land was dry again. There would be a few days rest for the horses, but other work was found for the horsemen. The next implement used was a skim, similar to a drag but instead of long teeth a blade 6′ x 3″ was attached to it and this disturbed any weeds which had taken root. On some farms it was policy to spread manure on a field and then plough it in. It was obtained from the midden created in the winter. The straw among it had perished and also any weed seeds. The manure was so rotten it integrated with the soil to disappear.

A flat roller in use at Millington Grange in 1920. The furrows were levelled after being processed with a set of light harrows. A flat roller followed and to complete the cultivation the land was harrowed again. On a hot summer day I have seen sweat rise from the horses' collars but they still plodded on across the field at a regular, steady, pace, and our shirt sleeves were much in evidence. Horses fared best when there were oats available to feed them at noon. Otherwise they were put into a pasture to graze for an hour which was not sufficient time for them to fill their bellies.

At work with a muck drill on Wold farm, 1925. When I was the wagoner at Wold Farm the 19th century drill was still in use as was the case with the corn seed drills where three horses were required, and four hands when it was in operation. It was referred to as a "muck" drill. During the winter a compost heap was accumulated in a lean-to shed. It comprised hen manure and small pieces collected after the fold yard or other buildings had been cleared of straw manure. When winter ploughing was held up the hired hands were detailed to turn the compost over several times until the contents became dry and crumbly. The drill resembled a cart to some extent and at the rear were two rows of spouts three in each one. The foreman stood on a step to ensure there was a continuous flow down the spouts.

Rowing plough and bobbing drill, as they appeared at the Yorkshire Show in 1970. In 1927 I had my only experience of sowing turnip seed by means of a bobbing drill and a rowing plough. On this farm the land had a good depth of soil free from clay and other heavy substances. After the land had been cultivated it was "rowed up" and a special plough was used to make the rows. The coulter was not required and the wheels were the same size. Instead of one mould board, there were two. I enjoyed this work beginning at one side of a field and continuing to the other. There was a marker on the plough which enabled me to create rows the correct width. Manure was carted from the fold-yard and spread evenly between the rows by men using pitch-forks. I followed with the plough which split the rows down the middle, and again rows were created which contained the manure on which the seed was sown. The two iron bobbins fixed to the drill turned on the rows and created a firm seed bed. Two spouts were attached to the seed box and each one fitted into a coulter. The seed was sown in the same manner as when a muck drill was in operation. The drill was a one-man, one-horse affair, and when in operation the horse walked between two rows and the wheels of the drill followed likewise. Although more preparation was required when this method of sowing was practiced, good results were obtained. Fold-yard manure stimulated the growth of the young plants and enriched the land too.

Mr. Starkey and the restored implements. I came across these two implements in a hedge bottom on Mr. Starkey's Preston Farm.
With his permission and the help of friends, I was able to restore them. Mr. Starkey's father bought them when they were on view
at the Yorkshire Show in 1930. In 1970, 40 years later, they appeared at the show again on the Yorkshire Farm Machinery
Preservation Society's stand.

Reaping a crop of oats. The driver is controlling the horses from a seat on the binder. To obtain the best results it was essential to complete the sowing of turnips in June and this brought to an end the cultivation of the fallows. The leaves of the swede turnips — the seed was the first to be sown —were spreading across the rows, covering the brown earth. In July the horses were enjoying a well-earned rest in the pasture. The corn had shot its ears and these were gradually turning from green to a golden colour showing promise of a good harvest. A field of ripening corn can be an attractive sight but nowadays it is often marred by tracks made by tractor wheels when spraying. The width of the corn rows has been reduced, and the movement of the stems are restricted. Corn is seldom seen swaying in a breeze, creating ripples across a field. A crop of oats, the most attractive cereal, has become a rare sight. A distinctive rustle could be heard when the ears were subjected to a breeze. Some old-lime farmers looked upon corn growing on their land as if it had been hallowed ground. Vehicle wheels were not allowed to turn on it

A typical Sunday School outing scene at Kilham, a Yorkshire Wold village, in the summer of 1915. July was the month when anniversary services were held in village chapels. Kirby Misperton chapel was well supported and on anniversary day relatives and friends from neighbouring villages arrived to attend the services. The chapel was full to overflowing and part of the congregation had to stand outside. The scholars' reward for their endeavour was an outing to a field on the outskirts of the village. They and their teachers travelled in two waggons owned by local farmers which had been washed or repainted for the occasion. The horses and harnesses were decorated and the brasses glistened in the sunshine. On arrival at the field sports and games were organised and tea was served before the return journey. In 1921 when bus services came into operation this happy event came to an end. The scholars were taken further afield and some saw the sea for the first time.

Chapter 9
When the Horse was King of the Shows

At the Pocklington show in 1920, the horse featured on the photograph was a winner in its class of best decorated horse. This took place in an era when the main mode of road transport was horse-drawn vehicles. Farmers relied on horses to till the land and farm workers' only official holiday was Christmas Day; but the majority of farmers would allow men time off to visit a show. In these days the heavy horse was king of the shows, but it was the hired horsemen who prepared them. They were never worked unless it was necessary and several evenings each week the horses were brought into the stable to be fed, groomed and their legs washed. The evening before the show the horses were completely washed and kept in the stable overnight. This attention was necessary because judges would not look twice at a horse in poor condition.

A pure bred Clydesdale mare, *Topsy*. The grey mare featured was bred on a stud farm in the York area and would have been retained as a brood mare if she had not been barren. A Hull coal merchant bought her and at the Cottingham Horse Show in 1934 she won the highest award. The owner is featured with the mare in hand, and holding the cup is a retired L.N.E.R. drayman who was responsible for preparing the mare. The harness had been taken to bits and every piece cleaned and polished including the buckles. Farmers whose horses were regularly exhibited owned special harnesses, only used on show days and similar occasions. This fine Clydesdale mare was a worthy winner.

Hull Brewery dray horses in the 1930s. Today's Shire horses enjoy a pleasant and easy life. Breeding for profit, for exhibiting or to advertise a product are the main reasons for their existence. Very few horses are trained to work on the land and are sold as dray horses. A pair owned by a brewery are only required to pull a vehicle carrying two tons. This was not the case in the pre-combustion era, when a pair of horses might be yoked to a dray loaded with five tons. When these horses were in their hey-day an agricultural show was held in every market town and in the largest villages, when in the region of fifty horses were exhibited. There were classes for foals and their mothers and every age group to five years. There was a special cup for the owner of the horse judged to be the best in the show. There was a class for the best decorated horse in cart harness, and likewise in a pair of plough gears.

Harry Chambers with his mare *Swanland Dale Beauty*. In the 1950s when Shire horses were gradually being replaced with machines Harry Chambers was one of the few farmers who retained the old brood mare and so saved the breed from extinction. He has played a major part in the Shires' survival. The horses Harry breeds and exhibits are always among the winners at all the main shows in the Ridings including the Yorkshire Show. Harry's horses are kept in separate fields according to their age group. When he calls them by name they each make their way to the gate. This particular morning a black mare, a prolific winner, did not respond, being unable to walk. An incurable injury was diagnosed and she was transported to a centre where unwanted horses were collected for export. Fortunately there was a waiting period and during that short spell the mare became sound again. Harry would not have known this had he not met a friend at Otley Show who informed him. He arranged for the mare to be brought home but she was in a sorry state. Her legs were cut and bruised due to the rough treatment she had received from the other horses. Time and the treatment she received from Harry healed the wounds, but she did not reach peak condition until the following year when once again she was among the winners.

A Hackney stallion, Supreme Champion at Doncaster Show in 1913. The Shires may have created the most interest when paraded in a show-ring but it was the Hackney high-steppers which were the most attractive. Harry Webster of Abbey Farm bred this type of horse and exported the stallions to Argentina. He visited this country when his services as a judge were required. A Hackney horse received special treatment when being prepared for a show. Elastic straps were attached to its front fetlocks and fastened to its body harness. This procedure encouraged it to raise its legs as high as possible. The horse was also shod with heavy shoes. On the morning of the Show these were replaced with plates and this procedure gave the horse extra buoyancy. When yoked to a jig a Hackney was a joy to drive and its beautiful action, a joy to watch. In the Depression of the 1920s there was no place for such luxury horses and by the 1930s they had become a rare sight. John Webster's main interest was breeding prize short-horn cattle, the pride of Yorkshire farmers. His bulls were in great demand by neighbours for breeding purposes.

This pair, in plough gears and owned by Harry Chambers, were first prize winners at the Driffield Show in 1970. Driffield Show was recognised as one of the best in the North and East Riding of Yorkshire and the Wold wagoners among the best horsemen. Proof of this was the high class of horses they exhibited. The majority of the judges were horse dealers, examining horses being their business. The majority of spectators are ignorant of the good points the judges are interested in. The exception are the men in the twilight of their lives who tilled the land with horses or those who left the farms to live in a town to drive horses yoked to drays. They can recall a sunny day when they had paraded horses round a Show ring or watched the various classes being judged — perhaps some consolation for the holidays they missed in their younger days.

Abbey Farm, prize short-horn bull, 1919. The classes for hunters attracted the least number of spectators. Few hired horsemen were interested. As could be expected the majority of the spectators were gentlemen farmers and others who followed the hounds on horse-back. Harry Webster left the management of his farm to his brother John, and he was more concerned with the prize short-horn cattle he bred, the pride of Yorkshire farmers.

Winner at the Yorkshire Show at Beverley in 1911. The saddle horse was five years old, the far wheeler three and the pair of lead horses each four years old. Today the Yorkshire Show has a permanent base, but in the early decades it was held in a different town or city each year. The horses and wagon featured in the photograph were first prize winners in their class when the Show was held at Beverley in 1911. The passing of the horse put paid to almost all the village shows. The one held at Thornton Dale has survived and on the day crowds pack the field. There is not a Shire horse to be seen, proof that the breed has become extinct in the area. A modern show does not appeal to me, having become too commercialised. The old-time comradeship is missing.

Crowds wait to welcome the Hayriders on Beverley Westwood. If there had not been any caring farmers and the heavy-horse breed had become extinct it would have been impossible to have organised the Walkington Hayride, a procession of old-time vehicles drawn by horses, held in June each year. On its way to Beverley Westwood, spectators line the route and pack the villages. When I received an invitation to take part in this charitable event, I accepted without hesitation. When I arrived at Woodland Farm, preparing the horses to the standard required in a show ring was well under way in the stackyard. Soon after 1.00 p.m. the procession began, the villagers dressed in clothes similar in style to those worn by the Victorians. I was most interested in the horses pulling the waggon, a carriage pair, the property of Mr. Cammage, a noted exhibitor at agricultural shows. He informed me the near-side horse *Squire* was four years old, and its partner ten years old. It had been a red-letter day. Once again I had travelled in a farm waggon, heard the rumbling of waggon wheels and the resounding noise created when iron shoes made contact with a hard road. I was reminded of days of long ago when I had driven a pair of horses yoked to a waggon, but my passengers had been children enjoying their Sunday School outing.

One of the first combine harvesters to be used in this country. The method of harvesting corn was constantly changing from approximately 1850 until combines appeared on the farms during the 1950s. With one of these machines corn is cut and threshed in one operation and a harvest is completed in a matter of days. The corn is not subjected to such long periods of wet weather. Moisture in the corn can be removed by artificial means. In the past when corn was cut with a reaper, sheaves produced and stooked and eventually contained in stacks, a farmer had to rely on the sun and wind to dry his corn. It was essential to cut the corn when it was dry, otherwise sprouts would soon appear among the ears. It was an exceptionlly fine time when all was gathered in within a month. Prior to the second half of the 19th century, corn was mown with a scythe, sheaves formed and tied by hand. The 'Gatherer' who followed the mower used a rake which consisted of three metal tines, nine inches long the width between each one four inches. The last in line was the 'Tier'. He encircled the loose sheaf with a corn band and twisted the ears together a certain way which produced a knot.

A Tip-reaper in 1850, the first corn reaper in general use. The first corn-reaper in general use appeared during the second half of the last century and was called a 'Tip-off' or 'Put-off' reaper. It was drawn by two horses and power was provided by means of a cog wheel fixed to the right-hand side travelling wheel. Two seats were fixed to the reaper. The driver rode on one and the 'tipper' on the other. As the corn was cut it dropped onto a platform made of lats. It was the 'Tipper's' job to rake sufficient corn together to form a sheaf and then tip it off the platform.

A sail-reaper, which followed the tip-reaper. The 'Sail' reaper, which appeared later, was an improvement because it could be operated by one man, the driver. The sails replaced the 'Tipper'. As these turned each one swept sufficient corn off the platform to form a sheaf. No doubt less time was required to cut a field of corn with a reaper but the sheaves still had to be tied by hand. Each 'Tier' was allocated a certain length on the side or across the end of the crop. When this procedure was practiced there was always a clear path for the horses drawing the reaper.

This picture of a Massey Harris self-binder shows the revolving canvasses and tin box containing the twine. The former method of harvesting corn continued until Massey Harris Binders appeared at the turn of the century. When one of these machines was in operation corn was cut, packed into sheaves and tied, thus reducing a farmer's costs. He no longer had to employ harvesters to tie bands round the sheaves.

The machinery was set in motion by interlocking cog wheels. The master was turned by means of a chain connected to the travelling wheel. This was the main support of the binder and was fixed to the frame beneath the packing table. At the cutting end was a small wheel and a divider. The latter parted the standing corn from that being cut. A small lever put in reverse disconnected the main cog wheel and neutralised the machine. The cutting width was six feet and the knife-bar passed through pointed sheaths at such a high speed it was impossible to see the triangular blades fixed to it. The sheaths also protected the blades from stones or other objects they might encounter.

The sails, turning antic-clockwise, pressured the corn as it was cut onto a moving platform, a broad canvas attached to two revolving wooden rollers. This carried the corn towards two more similar canvasses which turned alternate ways to form an elevator. The corn continued on its way between the canvasses until it reached the packing table where sheaves were produced and tied. When each one was completed, it was flung from the binder by three iron rotating arms.

Four horses yoked to a Massey Harris binder, on Hagg House Farm. 1925. The operator rode on a seat fixed at the rear of the binder and at hand were three levers. One enabled him to adjust the height of the sails according to the length of the corn. The second lever was used to adjust the packing table. Failure to do this could result in the sheaves being tied too near the ears or vice-versa, instead of in the middle. The third lever enabled the operator to raise or lower the points and cutting bar. When these were raised less power was required when the binder was being turned at the corners of the crop. The twine used to tie the sheaves was advertised by the trade as binder twine, but on most farms it was referred to as Massey Harris Band. Each ball weighed seven pounds and eight were delivered in one sack. Four horses were required and they were yoked to the binder in a similar manner as when a team was yoked to a waggon. The two lead horses were coupled together. The driver rode the near-side pole horse and drove the leading pair from this position.

Reaping completed with a Deering binder, 1930. On big farms, where the number of horses made this arrangement possible, two teams of four horses were allocated to one binder. Each team pulled the binder, three to four horses as required, and then were exchanged. The horses unyoked were returned to the stable to feed and rest. The cutting width was six feet and the overall operational width was ten feet. It was impossible to move the machine in this position from one field to another, the gate ways being too narrow. The binder was conveyed lengthways on a wooden bogey mounted on two iron wheels. It was upended onto the travelling wheel and the bogey pushed underneath it. When the binder was lowered the iron angles on the frame fitted into notches on the bogey and the binder was made secure. The pole attached to the cutting end completed the operation referred to as 'Packing Up'. Two horses could pull the bogey carrying the binder and on arrival at the next field this operation took place in reverse. Before the 1914-18 War improved models became available. The bogey was replaced with two wheels which could be attached to the binder's frame and there was no need to upend it. During this period 'Deerings' produced a binder not as heavy as a Massey Harris. Three horses could pull one and some operators drove them from the seat on the binder.

An unusual 1920s photo, because the driver is riding the far-side horse. When the sun was shining, the corn standing, the land dry, and a breeze blowing which benefited the horses, driving four horses yoked to a binder was a pleasure. Conditions were completely different when wet weather frequently interfered with operations. Cutting the corn became a hard slog for men and horses. Occasionally a storm flattened the crops and the mis-shaped sheaves produced were awkward to handle through all the stages, stooking, loading and stacking. The corn could only be cut with a binder when the ears were pointing towards the knife. Otherwise the corn had to be lifted and turned towards the approaching binder using appropriate sticks. Sun and wind could not penetrate the laid corn and the wet soil stuck to the travelling wheel. If this was allowed to accumulate the wheel would not have turned. There were occasions when the twisted corn blocked the canvas elevator and this had to be removed, sheaves formed and tied by hand. There were continual stoppages, and before the binder was moved forward it was necessary to reverse it in order to start the machinery. More effort was required from the horses and this sapped their energy. They were worked to their full capacity, unable to pull the binder at the same speed as they could when the land was dry and the corn standing.

One of the first self-binders and tractors to be invented.

One of the last corn-reaping outfits in operation before the advent of the combine harvester. Misty mornings and a heavy dew were often experienced during a harvest. There was not a breath of wind. All was so quiet and still that you could hear the stubble snap under your feet. Spiders had been busy during the early hours and cobwebs hung across the doors of farm buildings. Those hanging on hedges between the corn fields resembled lace curtains, and dewy dark-coloured brambles peeped through them. When the sun broke through the mist it came into sight instantly with the promise of a fine day. Married workers were engaged for a 'harvest month' for a sum of money above their normal weekly rate and at this stage stooking the sheaves was the main work in hand.

A group of harvesters, early this century. The method practiced by stookers was universal on all farms. Two men worked as a team and each stook contained five pairs of sheaves. Six rows of sheaves were made into one row of stooks and this was sited between the third and fourth row of sheaves. This procedure evened the distance each stooker had to carry the sheaves. Although interest was created siting the stooks as straight as possible, the work was tedious and tiring.

If the sheaves had been subjected to a heavy rain the conditions were unpleasant too. A man could pick up by the ears a barley or oat sheaf, and carry one in each hand to a stook without touching his body. This was impossible with long heavy wheat sheaves and a stooker's clothes were affected. There was no specified protective clothing available.

To obtain the best results from the sun and wind wet stooks were pulled over and the sheaves spread on the ground and later re-stooked. The young clover crop which covered the barley stubble caused problems. In the spring the seed had been sown among the young barley and this was the result. If wet weather delayed leading, the stooks had to be re-sited or the clover roots under each one would have perished.

When the weather continued to be favourable, this work was not necessary. No time was lost or costs increased and no damage was done. Persistant rain, however, could ruin the crops. The 1927 harvest was the worst I experienced. When I left the farm on Martinmas Day, 23rd November, I recall seeing stooks rotting in a field.

Chapter 11
Harvesting, Leading and Stacking

Loading corn at Mr. Starkey's Rose Hill Farm, Preston, in 1930. Leading sheaves home and stacking them was the second stage of harvest, but as usual the weather played an important part. It was essential that the sap had dried out of the stalks and the sheaves were completely dry. Otherwise a combustion would be created in the stack. When vapour appeared out of the top of one, a farmer had no option but to re-stack the sheaves on another site. While this was in progress sacks full of straw were pulled up through the stack to provide ventilation. When the corn was thrashed it had little selling value and when ground into meal was poor fodder for stock. Wagoners who loaded their vehicles preferred pole-wagons when travelling from a field with a load. They could ride their near-side horse. They used to compete with each other to see which one could make the most attractive loads, although on arrival at the stackyard each one in due course disappeared into a stack. Before loading began certain preparations took place. Waggon wheels were oiled, turn-tables greased and a pair or ropes hung on the back of each wagon required to make a load secure. Two tined forks, the handles of various lengths, which had not been used since the previous harvest, were brought out of storage. Each man picked the type of fork he required and used it throughout the harvest. There was one a 'nine pinta', so called because the handle was nine feet long. It was used to fork the sheaves to the highest point on a stack. It was hard luck for a lad after a hard day's work if he had to use this fork to team his last load. Sites in the stackyard for the rows of stacks, with space between them for a threshing machine to operate, were measured in strides by the Foreman. The base, referred to as a 'Steddle', for each stack was covered with a thick layer of straw to ensure the first layer of sheaves did not come into contact with the damp ground. The workforce was organised into teams of five and the total number depended on the size of the farm. Each team consisted of a stacker and a picker who supplied the stacker with sheaves from the position where they were teamed onto the stack, also a forker who worked in the field and supplied the loaders with sheaves, and two hired horsemen and their waggons. When leading was in progress from a far field another loader and waggon were required on account of the longer distance to the farm.

Horses feeding at noon, still yoked to their wagon. A forker was supplied with his meals in the field, and while a wagoner consumed his a spare hand teamed the load. While this was taking place the horses, which were not unyoked during the day, were feeding on tares contained in a barrow placed near their heads. They were supplied with water which they drank out of a bucket. The stacker and picker ate their meals in the interval between the arrival of a load. It was remarkable how soon a field was cleared when there were no interruptions. When loading was in full swing the roads and by-lanes were alive with men and horses and wagons. Before motor transport became established a wagoner drove his team yoked to a loaded waggon out of a field onto a road confident no other traffic would bar his way.

A typical load of corn sheaves early this century. Loading bales of straw on a tractor trailer is a simple affair when compared to loading sheaves on a farm waggon. Special knowledge and practice were required to load three hundred sheaves on a waggon. It was essential if the load was to 'carry' that it should be built plum on the waggon and that each sheaf loaded should bind the previous one. Even when a load was inclined to lean to one side of the waggon it would 'carry' if the sheaves held firm and did not slip. The body of the waggon was packed first. Then sheaves were placed on the shelvings and across each end. They overlapped to some extent, enabling a load to be made longer and wider than the waggon. When the middle was packed the outside sheaves were made secure. The base for the load was complete and was referred to as a 'square course'. After three had been completed the load took on a different pattern. The sheaves were placed lengthways. The loader worked from the front of the waggon to the back and vice-versa. Double rows were placed across each end, the ears pointing inwards. It was essential to make the ends higher than the middle, thus reducing the danger of them sagging and eventually slipping off, and to pack the sheaves in the middle as firm as possible to hold the end sheaves in position. This pattern of loading was known as 'shipping'. Eventually the load was made narrower until a single row of sheaves completed it. Then it was tied down with two ropes and made ready for the journey home to the stack. There were no springs on a waggon, which registered every depression in the field often shaking the loads.

More sheaves could be loaded on a trailer towed by a tractor. When travelling in the ruts down a lane a waggon creaked and rolled. The load swayed from one side to another. No wonder a young lad turned in his saddle and looked back anxiously to see if any sheaves were slipping. There were occasions when loads tipped over but this did not affect horses yoked to a pole-waggon. When shafts were attached to one, however, the horse between them was thrown onto its side. Sometimes a lad would arrive at the stack the front of his load intact but not knowing the back end had slipped off until the foreman shouted, "Where is your back end, lad?" He was not rebuked for this mishap. The foreman could not send any Tom, Dick or Harry to a field with a waggon, load it with sheaves and bring it safely home. Loading a waggon began at the farside of a field and it was completed as near the gate as possible. There was no sense in finishing a load in the middle of a field. The horses had a long day ahead and pulling a load this extra distance was wasted energy. The forker had certain responsibilities and when possible a man who had been a wagoner in his younger days was chosen for this job. He knew the correct way to load a waggon and could handle the horses which he drove from one stook to another by word or mouth. It was essential that each load contained the same number of sheaves, to retain the rhythm of the turn-round. While one wagoner teamed his load the other was loading his waggon in the field. A forker had to take into consideration the state of the land and assess the size of the loads accordingly. When the land was dry the horses could pull bigger loads than when it was soft going. If a waggon was bogged down, time was lost and the horses suffered. Credit was due to them and their drivers for the manner in which loads were pulled out of a field under these conditions. Only men who experienced those by-gone harvesting days know what big hearts the horses had. A good forker could cut down to a minimum the time required to load a waggon with sheaves. He forked two at a time and he knew which way the ears should point. As soon as a loader had pressed them down in position two more were at hand. A lad who was a learner relied on the forker to help him and he could not have had a better instructor. He kept his eye on the progress of the load and ensured it was taking shape plum on the waggon. He pushed a bulging corner in with his fork and when one was completed he roped it down. Leading continued until it was too dark to see and no lamps were carried on a waggon. I recall after completing a load how difficult it was to see the gateway into the field. When passing through one it was not unusual for a waggon wheel to crash into a post and break it off at ground level. Should this occur another loader would be sure to brag, "'One night I knocked both posts down". Last loads and the stack in progress were sheeted down and the stackers had to feel their way down the ladders. Horses were unyoked with the aid of stable lamps. They were free from sweat and for this reason could immediately be stripped of their harness and turned into the pasture. After supper had been served bedtime was drawing near for the harvesters.

Teaming a load of corn and stacking the sheaves. Building a corn stack was highly skilled work, true craftsmanship. A farmer would not consider a man to be his Foreman if he was unable to stack. The construction of a stack was a remarkable achievement because it provided a store house for the produce used to built it. It also took shape under the stacker's feet. Some were so confident the stack was taking the correct shape they could complete one without coming down to ground level to inspect its progress. I never shared this confidence. The sheaves varied in size. It was impossible to assess the correct number but several thousand were made into a solid weatherproof unit. This was most important should rain water seep into a stack, when untold damage was done to the grain. It was unsaleable and when ground into meal was poor fodder for cattle. A stacker worked in the same manner as when loading a waggon. Each sheaf, as it was laid, bound the previous one. The outside rows had the ears pointing inwards. This formed the shape and was referred to as the 'outside course'. The next row of sheaves overlapped the outside ones half-way. He continued in this fashion until the centre of the stack was reached. The stacker walked on every sheaf and the whole layer was firm and compact. He continued this procedure until the stack reached a required height, making sure the outside rows of sheaves were level. If they dipped inwards rainwater would be able to enter the stack. Stacking the middle was important for this matter alone and learners were advised, "stack the middle right and the outside sheaves will stack themselves."

Every picture is supposed to tell a story and this photograph is no exception. It was taken during the first decade of this century and it illustrates a typical harvest scene of the period. It can be assumed the corn had been cut, sheaves produced and stooked and a start made to lead the sheaves home. On this particular morning, when the lads had brought the horses from the pasture to the stable, the grass was heavy with dew and the sheaves were in a similar state. The horses were enoying a well-earned rest until the Foreman decided, after they had been yoked to the waggons in readiness and lunch had been consumed, the sheaves would be dry. Meanwhile, the horses waited patiently. The stance of the 'old uns' nearest the camera gives the impression they were tired but this was not always the case. They were wise, having learned over the years to stand in the most relaxed position. Pulling a binder had been a hard slog. Usually an 'old un' was selected to be the saddle-horse which carried the driver and this was an extra burden, but from now on until the end of the harvest life was to become easier and it was remarkable how soon the old horses picked up again. When leading the sheaves home was in progress there were rest times for the horses when a load was being teamed onto a stack.

Topping up a stack. The bole was the bottom part of a stack and the width had been expanded to form eaves. It was then provided with a roof and the procedure practiced was referred to as 'topping up'. Because the bole was wider at the eaves than the base, rainwater ran down the roof and dropped direct to the ground. If the 'topping up' was done in the correct manner, the contents would not be affected regardless of the weather conditions. The middle was built up first to enable the outside rows of sheaves to be laid at a similar angle as the tiles on a house. The stacker walked backwards and packed the sheaves as close together as possible. Gradually the stack was made narrow and the roof began to take shape. When it was completed the top, known as the rig, was the width of the last row of sheaves and these were covered with straw. After the last load of sheaves had been brought home a start was made to prepare the stacks for thatching. Loose corn was raked off the roofs and the protruding ends of sheaves pushed inwards with forks. Wheat and oat stacks required little attention, but a hedge-slasher may have been necessary to trim the bulging corners of barley stacks. Due to the smooth texture of the straw, barley sheaves were the most difficult to stack. They were inclined to slip and it was not unusual for a learner to see a corner of his stack slip onto the ground. Wheat straw which had been prepared by removing the shortest straws was used as thatch. This had taken place when wet weather held up harvest operations and was referred to as 'drawing straw'.

Mr. R. Watts, the thatcher at work on Ridge Mount Farm, 1912, on a humble-end stack. There was a certain amount of pressure on a thatcher's knees when they made contact with the ladder. To protect them he made pads with straw and sackcloth which he made secure with Massey Harris binder twine. He also used this to secure the thatch to the stack. The twine was tied to the end of 'stack prods', small hazel branches cut out of hedgerows. A man thatched as far as he could reach usually the double width of the ladder. The first course consisted of a number of handfuls of straw, the ends of each one turned back before they were pushed into the eaves of the stack. The following courses were laid flat, the straw as straight as possible.

Thatching a corn pike at Rectory Farm. Thornton le Dale in 1920. Each course overlapped the other. The last one covered the ridge and was fastened down at each side of the stack. As the thatcher came down his ladder he made each course secure using the stack prods and twine. Then the ladder was moved to a fresh position and the thatching continued in this manner until the roof of the stack was covered. It was a pleasure to thatch on a calm day and there was a sense of satisfaction, in knowing the contents of the stack would retain its quality until threshing took place. During the Depression experienced in the 1920s, many farmers, in order to economise, reduced their labour force. Instead of trimming and thatching the stacks each one was covered with a load of straw held in position with nets. A heap was a most appropriate name.

Corn Pikes at Weghill Farm, Preston, in 1930. There were three types of stacks on farms in Yorkshire; 'Pikes', 'Gable-end' and 'Humble-end'. The majority contained sufficient sheaves which required a day to thresh them. The round Pikes built with wheat sheaves were the show pieces in the stackyard and were very popular with the farmers in the North and East Ridings of Yorkshire. The last course of thatch laid on a Pike was covered with an umbrella made with straw called a 'Mopin' and this brought the stack to a point. It was not unusual to see the iron figure of a cockerel or fox protruding from it. Gable-end stacks may have obtained this name because their shape was similar to the houses of that name. Only the sides of the roof were thatched, the ends were left bare. A strong wind might lift the thatch and enable rainwater to penetrate into the stack. Gable-end stacks were built in good sheltered stackyards.

Model stacks made by Herbert Day from straw, From left to right: Gable-end, Pike and Humble-end. The name Humble-end was an appropriate name for this type of stack because of its plain appearance. It was sometimes called a coupen stack because sections were added on to make it longer. These stacks were recognised as the least difficult to stack. It was for this reason barley sheaves, which were inclined to slip, were contained in them. A Humble-end stack was built on an oblong 'steddle' and there were no actual corners. When the bole was being topped up the ends were drawn inwards in the same manner as the sides. When the roof of one of these stacks was thatched it was completely covered and the strongest winds could not dislodge the thatch. On moorland farms situated on high ground there was little shelter in the stackyards. All the corn was built into Humble-end stacks.

All is safely gathered in and the thatched stacks "appt doon". After the advent of the combine harvester farms were completely mechanised and the end of the day for the horse was in sight. The stacking and thatching skills of yesterday's harvesters were no longer required and these have practically died out too. The picturesque stacking scenes created before farms were mechanised will never be witnessed again, nor will farmers today be subject to the problems experienced in the past when the weather was unfavourable. A full stackyard was most attractive when the moon cast long dark shadows among them. On such a night the clear outline of the cornstacks, the sharp edge of the thatch and the mopins on the pikes pointing towards the sky, never failed to impress me.

Chapter 12
Sowing Wheat at Back-End

Harrowing at back-end on a Holderness farm in 1914. When the last stack of sheaves had been built the fields were horse-raked and the loose corn gathered. The brown earth was conspicuous between the rows of stubble. In the autumn sunshine these looked fresh and clean and were the colour of pale gold. Hares hopped across a field at their leisure and a partridge rose from the ground practically from under your feet. When the ploughs moved in, the stubble disappeared under the furrows, which did likewise under the harrows, when forming a seed bed in order to drill wheat. Ploughing for wheat at back-end was a welcome change from cultivating dusty fallows or harrowing.

Horses waiting patiently near the gate at Wold Farm in 1927. At this time of the year grass contained little nourishment and was poor fodder. I was just as keen to sleep the horses in the stable as I had been to turn them out in April. When we had walked to the gate to collect them we had found them grazing as far from the gate as possible. But on these dark and dismal, and often rainy mornings, the horses were waiting near the gate for us. The first two weeks when the horses slept in the stable were a difficult time. The change of diet from grass to dry hard fodder could cause disorders. Newly threshed oats were not seasoned and if a horse was not rationed it may be subjected to a complaint known as "humours". When the atmosphere was heavy horses were inclined to sweat. If their coats were wet at the end of the day I allowed them only a limited amount of water, as a bellyful could cause an attack of colic.

This drill was restored by the author. The sheaths are clearly visible, as are the cog wheels which turned the spindle on the seed-box. On the Wolds the method of sowing wheat was known as ploughing and pressing. Land was ploughed, drilled and harrowed in one single operation. The implement used was a unique affair and was called a press-drill. Fixed to the rear of an oblong frame was a seed box and at the front was a pair of shafts. The frame pivoted on an axle and iron wheels called sheaths turned on this. The width between each one was the same as the furrows being ploughed. Attached to the opposite end of the axle was a wheel which turned on the land. When the drill was in operation the pressure from the sheaths as they turned between the ridges created a depression into which the seed dropped. The harrow which followed completed the operation.

A press-drill at work on the Wolds in 1926. The number of horses required to pull a drill depended on the number of sheaths. These varied from two to four in order to correspond with the number of ploughs involved. The largest drills required three horses and a trace-horse was yoked at each side of the shaft-horse which walked down the furrows. Men and their teams crossing a field in line were an impressive sight. Brasses attached to the harnesses on the horses gleamed when the sun was shining. I recall how the gulls emitted their shrill cries as they flew and swooped over the horses' backs. Each furrow was ploughed straight and the result of this was the exactly corresponding rows of wheat seen throughout the following winter.

The old and the new. The Ferguson tractor was popular in the 1930s. No farming operation gave me more pleasure than this method of sowing wheat, but my most agreeable memory of those far-off days concerned field mice. These small animals were a common sight in the harvest fields. They made shallow warrens under oat stooks, and stored grain in them. When ploughing I have seen a mouse appear as if by magic out of a farrow as it was being turned over. It ran across the ridges stiff obstacles for an animal so small, but fear gave it strength. It was amusing to watch its head and tail bobbing up and down alternately. No doubt the hedge bottom was a welcome sight, a place where a mouse could spend the rest of the year until harvest came round again.

A country lane, enclosed with well-maintained hedgerows, typical of yesteryear. The sowing of wheat was the first contribution to another harvest, but there was no further cultivation or sowing until the Spring. The drills and harrows were put into storage for the winter. Martinmas Day (November 23rd) was drawing near when the hired hands would receive their yearly wage and perhaps be asked to return for another year. It was the beginning of their annual unpaid week's holiday when once again they could enjoy the comforts of homes. It passed so quickly and soon they were on their way to their places where they would live and work until Martinmas Day came round again. This custom of engaging men came to an end in the 1930s when tractors were making their mark on the land. Mechanisation has certainly changed conditions on farms and the work is no longer the drudgery it used to be. Threshing sets have become obsolete and the hard, unpleasant work involved when threshing a corn stack has come to an end. Practically all the hand tools used in the past have become obsolete. Fork-lifts have become available also muck-loaders and spreaders. Due to farming techniques the countryside has suffered unreparable damage. Instead of fields which when cropped with cereals or roots created a "crazy-paving" pattern across the countryside there are large areas of agricultural land barren of trees and hedges, and consequently nature has suffered. Eventually all the hired farm horsemen will have passed on, their knowledge and skill will die out. They lived in an era when life was slow and meaningful and the beauty of the countryside remained unspoiled.